Better Guitar With

Rockschool

A *Rockschool* Publication
Broomfield House, Broomfield Road, Richmond, Surrey TW9 3HS

Welcome To *Guitar* Grade 5

Welcome to the Rockschool *Guitar* Grade 5 pack. The book and CD contain everything needed to play guitar in this grade. In the book you will find the exam scores in both standard notation and TAB. The CD has full stereo mixes of each tune, backing tracks to play along with for practice and tuning notes. Handy tips on playing the pieces and the marking schemes can be found in the Guru's Guide on page 21. If you have any queries about this or any other Rockschool exam, please call us on **020 8332 6303** or email us at office@rockschool.co.uk or visit our website http://www.rockschool.co.uk. Good luck!

Performer Zone Techniques in Grade 4 and Grade 5

The eight Rockschool grades are divided into four Zones. *Guitar* Grade 5, along with Grade 4, is part of the *Performer Zone.* This Zone is for those of you who are confident in all the key skills on guitar and who are stepping up to more advanced skills and stylistic expression

Grade 4: in this grade you use a range of physical and expressive techniques with confidence, including damping and the use of double stops on adjacent strings, legato and staccato, slides, fretting hand and whammy vibrato, hammer-ons and pull-offs, and accents and you are experimenting with a range of dynamics from very quiet (*pp*) to very loud (*ff*). It is in this grade that you are continuing to develop your ability to play with stylistic authority.

Grade 5: as a player you will be confident in a range of physical and expressive techniques. You will be able to demonstrate your abilities across a number of styles and have control over sound and tone adjustments to suit the playing styles of your choice.

Performer Zone Guitar Exams

There are **three** types of exam that can be taken using this pack: Grade Exam, Performance Certificate and Band Exam.

• *Guitar* Grade 5 Exam: this is for players who want to develop performance and technical skills

Players wishing to enter for a *Guitar* Grade 5 exam need to prepare **three** pieces, of which **one** may be a free choice piece chosen from outside the printed repertoire. In addition, you must prepare the technical exercises in this book, undertake either a sight reading test or an improvisation & interpretation test, take an ear test and answer general musicianship questions. Samples of these are printed in the book.

• *Performer Zone* Performance Certificate in Guitar: this is for players who want to focus on performing in a range of styles

To enter for your *Performer Zone* Performance Certificate you play pieces only. You can choose any **five** of the six tunes printed in this book, or you can bring in up to **two** free choice pieces as long as they meet the standards set out in the Guru's Guide below.

• *Performer Zone* Band Exam in Guitar, Guitar and Drums: this is for players who want to play as a band

The *Performer Zone* Band Exam is for all of you who are in a group, and features guitar, bass and drums. You play together in the exam, using the parts printed in the Guitar, Bass and Drum books. Like the *Performer Zone* Performance Certificate, you play **five** of the six printed pieces, or you can include up to **two** free choice pieces as long as they meet the standards set out in the Guru's Guide below. If you take this exam you will be marked as a unit with each player expected to contribute equally to the overall performance of each piece played.

Guitar Tablature Explained
Guitar music in this book is notated in both standard notation and tablature

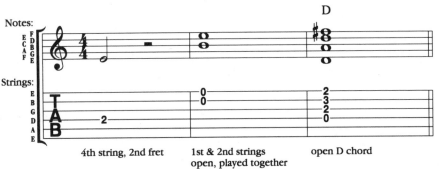

THE MUSICAL STAVE shows pitches and rhythms and is divided by lines into bars. Pitches are named after the first seven letters of the alphabet.

TABLATURE graphically represents the guitar fingerboard. Each horizontal line represents a string, and each number represents a fret.

4th string, 2nd fret   1st & 2nd strings open, played together   open D chord

Definitions For Special Guitar Notation

HAMMER ON: Pick the lower note, then sound the higher note by fretting it without picking.

PULL OFF: Pick the higher note then sound the lower note by lifting the finger without picking.

SLIDE: Pick the first note, then slide to the next with the same finger.

STRING BENDS: Pick the first note then bend (or release the bend) to the pitch indicated in brackets.

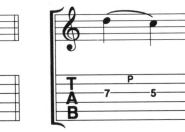

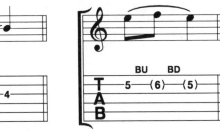

GLISSANDO: Pick the note and slide along the string in the direction indicated.

VIBRATO: Vibrate the note by bending and releasing the string smoothly and continuously.

TRILL: Rapidly alternate between the two bracketed notes by hammering on and pulling off.

NATURAL HARMONICS: Lightly touch the string above the indicated fret then pick to sound a harmonic.

PINCHED HARMONICS: Bring the thumb of the picking hand into contact with the string immediately after the pick.

PICK HAND TAP: Strike the indicated note with a finger from the picking hand. Usually followed by a pull off.

FRET HAND TAP: As pick hand tap, but use fretting hand. Usually followed by a pull off or hammer on.

QUARTER TONE BEND: Pick the note indicated and bend the string up by a quarter tone.

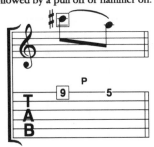

 (accent) • Accentuate note (play it louder).

 (accent) • Accentuate note with great intensity.

 (staccato) • Shorten time value of note.

 • Downstroke

V • Upstroke

D.%. al Coda

D.C. al Fine

tacet

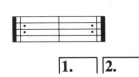

• Go back to the sign (%), then play until the bar marked *To Coda* ⊕ then skip to the section marked ⊕ *Coda*.

• Go back to the beginning of the song and play until the bar marked *Fine* (end).

• Instrument is silent (drops out).

• Repeat bars between signs.

• When a repeated section has different endings, play the first ending only the first time and the second ending only the second time.

Radioheads

Bernice Cartwright

Mud Pie

Hussein Boon

Downtime

Hussein Boon

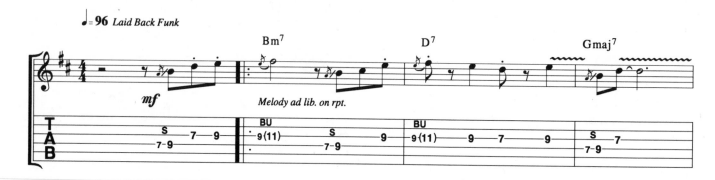

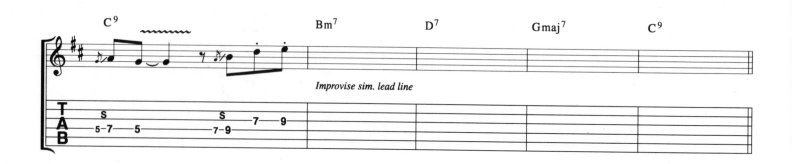

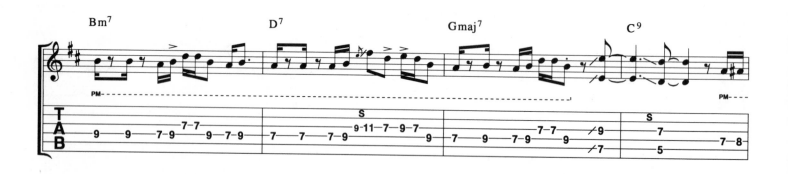

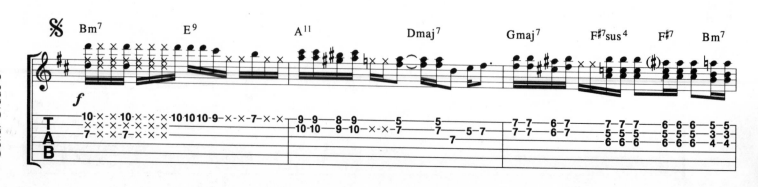

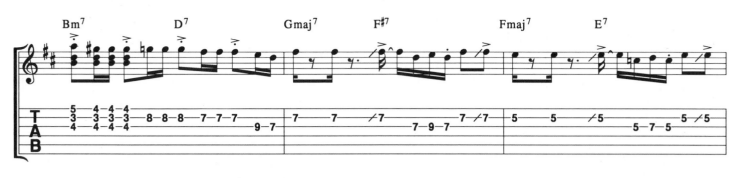

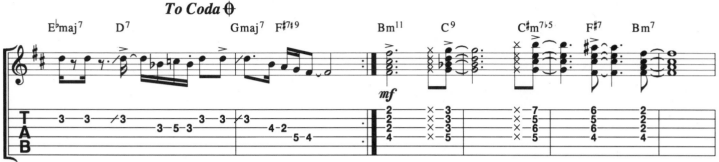

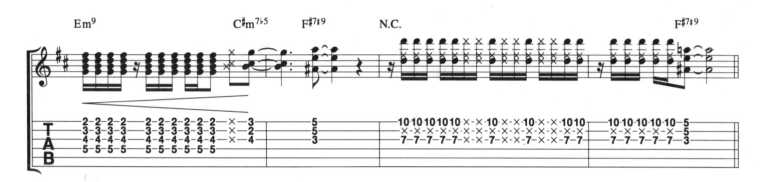

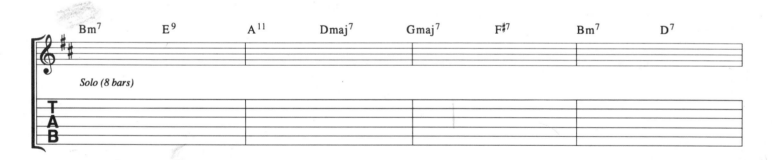

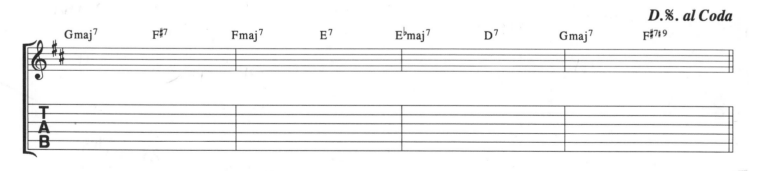

Queen For A Day

Deirdre Cartwright

♩=66 *Stadium Rock*

Freely & majestic

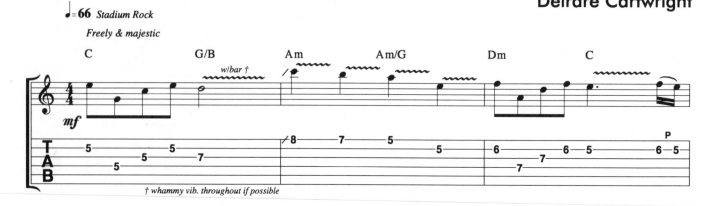

† *whammy vib. throughout if possible*

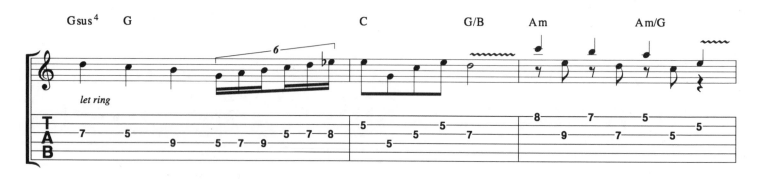

let ring

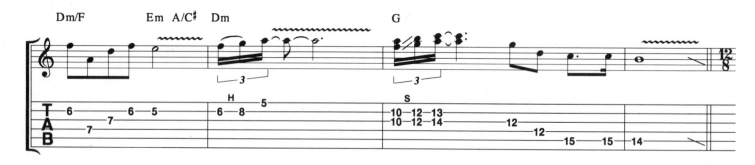

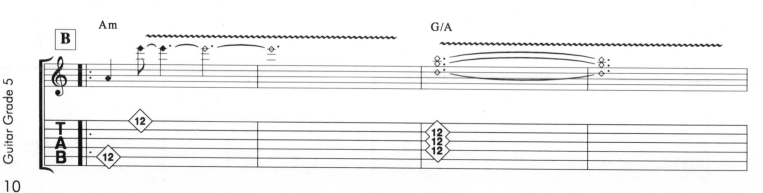

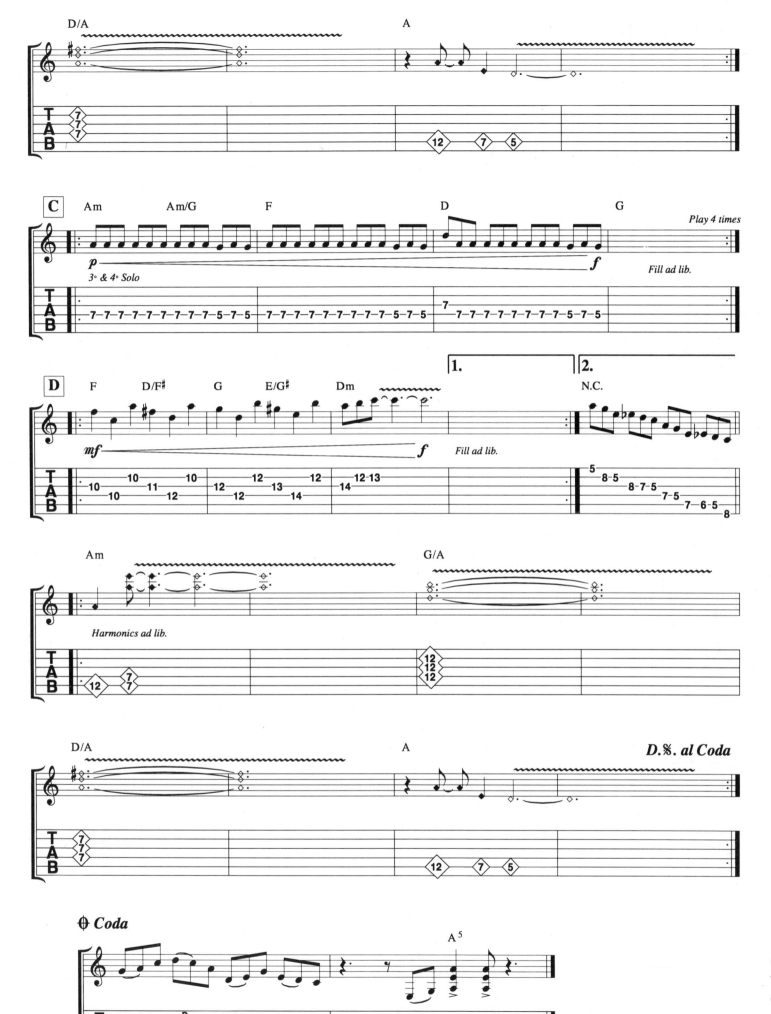

In The Bag

Steve Wrigley

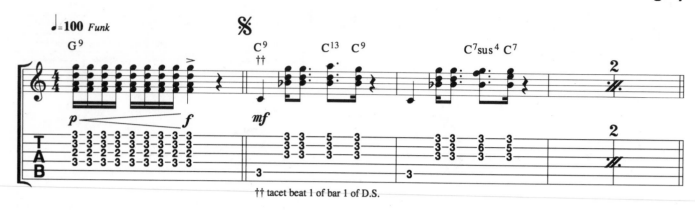

†† tacet beat 1 of bar 1 of D.S.

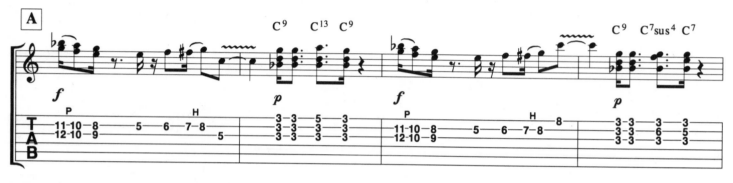

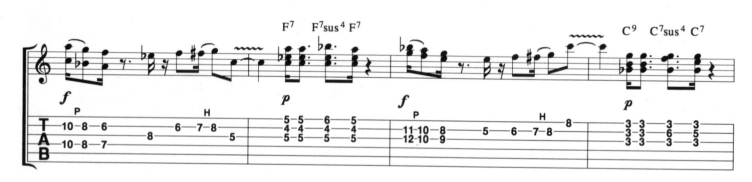

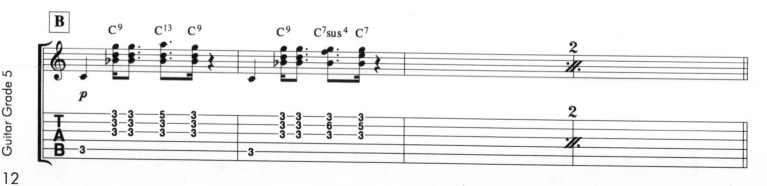

Rock Steady

Dave Barnard

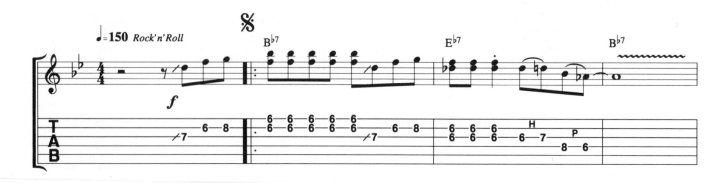

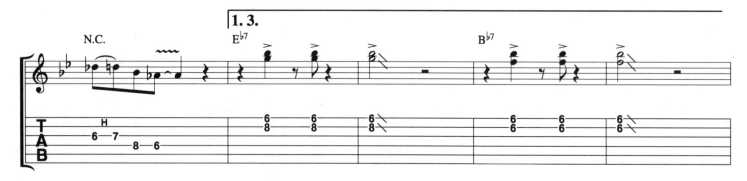

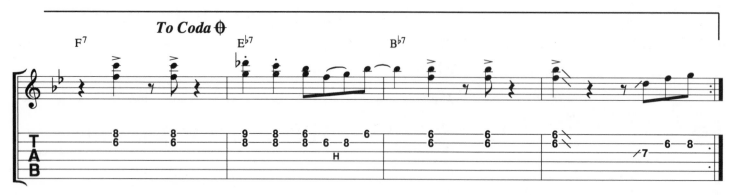

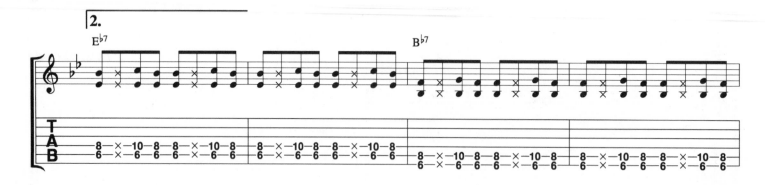

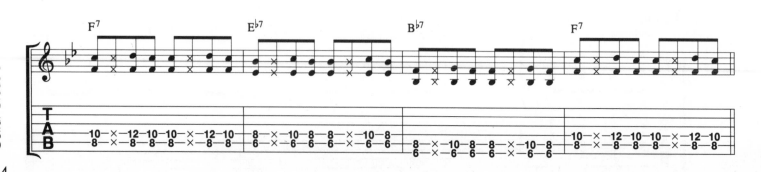

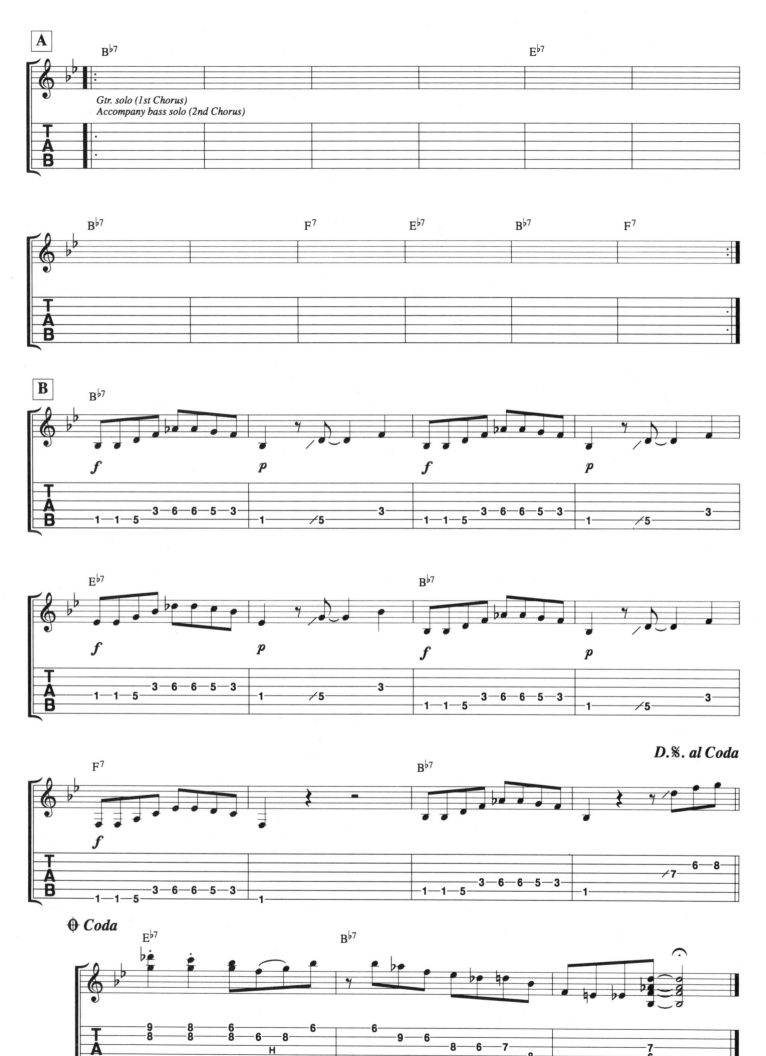

Technical Exercises

In this section, the examiner will ask you to play a selection of exercises drawn from each of the two groups shown below. These exercises contain examples of the kinds of scales and arpeggios you can use when playing the pieces. You do not need to memorise the exercises (and can use the book in the exam) but the examiner will be looking for the speed of your response. The examiner will also give credit for the level of your musicality.

The exercises should be prepared in the following keys: C, F, G, D, A, B♭, and cover at least 2 octaves, both ascending and descending. The TAB fingerings shown below are suggestions only. The exercises should be played at ♩=100. The examiner will give you this tempo in the exam.

Group A: Scales

Major scales

Root 6th

Root 5th

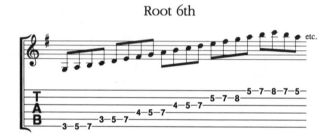
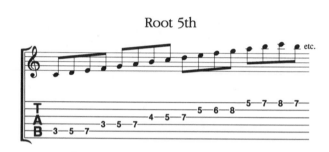

Minor pentatonic scales

Position 1

Position 2

Position 3

Position 4

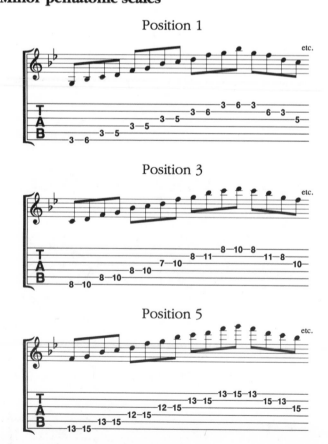

Position 5

Blues scales

Root 6th

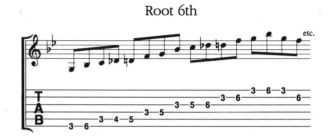

Root 5th

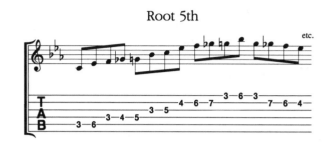

Modes of the major scale

Dorian mode

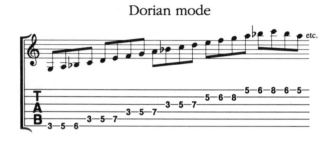

Mixolydian mode

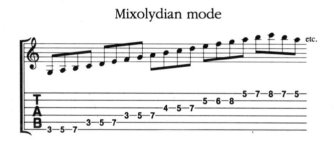

Group B: Arpeggios

Major 7th

Dominant 7th

Minor 7th

Sight Reading *or* Improvisation & Interpretation

In this section you have a choice between either a sight reading test or an improvisation & interpretation test. Printed below is an example of the type of **sight reading** test you are likely to encounter in the exam. This will be in one of the following styles: blues, rock, funk or jazz. The examiner will allow you 90 seconds to prepare it and will set the tempo for you on a metronome.

Printed below is an example of the type of **improvisation & interpretation** test you are likely to encounter in an exam. You will be asked to play an improvised line over a set of chord changes lasting 12 bars in one of the following styles: blues, rock, funk or jazz. The examiner will allow you 90 seconds to prepare it and will set the tempo for you on a metronome.

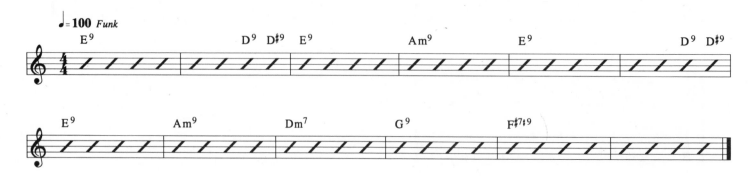

Ear Tests

You will find two ear tests in this grade. The examiner will play each test to you twice on CD. You will find two examples of the type of test you will get in the exam printed below.

Test 1

You will be asked to play back on your guitar a simple melody of not more than four bars composed from the diatonic notes from either C major, G major, Aminor or E minor. You will be given the tonic note and will hear the sequence twice. An example in A minor is shown below.

Test 2

You will also be asked to recognise a sequence of chords chosen from I, II minor, IV, V and VI minor in the keys of either D major, F major or C major. You will hear the sequence twice and you may use your guitar as a guide while the sequence is playing. An example in C major is shown below

General Musicianship Questions

You will be asked five General Musicianship Questions at the end of the exam.

Topics:

i)   Music theory
ii)   Knowledge of the candidate's instrument

The music theory questions will cover the following topics at this grade:

Recognition of pitches	Dynamic markings (*p*, *mp*, *mf* and *f*)
Note values	Repeat markings
Rests	Cresc. and dim.
Time signatures	Accents, staccato, vibrato
Key signatures	Hammer ons, pull offs
D.S. and D.C. al coda	Fermata (Pause)
Ral. and Rit.	

Knowledge of the construction of the following chord types:

Major	Major 7th	Dominant 7th
Minor	Minor 7th	Minor 7th♭5

Questions on these topics will be drawn from one of the pieces played you have played in the exam.

The instrument knowledge questions will cover the following topics at this grade:

Plugging into the amplifier and the guitar
Volume and tone adjustments on the guitar
Volume and tone adjustments on the amplifier

Knowledge of parts of the guitar guitar:

Fretboard, neck, body, tuning pegs, nut, pickups,
bridge, pickup selectors, scratchplate, and jack socket

Knowledge of main guitar makes

Knowledge of main pickup types

The Guru's Guide To *Guitar* Grade 5

This section contains some handy hints compiled by Rockschool's Guitar Guru to help you get the most out of the performance pieces. Do feel free to adapt the tunes to suit your playing style. Remember, these tunes are your chance to show your musical imagination and personality.

The TAB fingerings are suggestions only. Feel free to use different neck positions as they suit you. Please also note the solos featured in the full mixes are not meant to be indicative of the standard required for the grade.

Guitar Grade 5 Tunes

Rockschool tunes help you play the hit tunes you enjoy. The pieces have been written by top pop and rock composers and players according to style specifications drawn up by Rockschool.

The tunes printed here are divided into two groups of three pieces. The first group of pieces belongs to the *contemporary mainstream* and features current styles in today's charts. The second group of pieces consists of *roots styles*, those classic grooves and genres which influence every generation of performers.

CD full mix track 1, backing track 8: *Radioheads*

Brit Pop, Radiohead style. This part, with its 16th notes, and eighth and 16th note combinations, looks quite challenging on paper but many of these are repeated arpeggios. Watch for those bars of 7/8 slipped in to trip up the unwary. There is a six bar solo marked and you should also experiment with different amp sounds and dynamics.

Composer: Bernice Cartwright. Bernice is a successful bass player and composer with a string of TV and theatre credits to her name.

CD full mix track 2, backing track 9: *Mud Pie*∗

Modern Texas blues in style of the late Stevie Ray Vaughan (check out his *Scuttlebuttin'*). This is taken at quite a lick and the line needs practice to get absolutely right, but as it consists mainly of eighth notes with a couple of syncopations and triplets thrown in, it should be quite straightforward.

Composer: Hussein Boon. Hussein says he plays mainly "noisy pop" and the odd bit of drum 'n' bass. He has graced bands such as Beats International, Microgroove and De La Soul and artists such as Omar and Karen Ramirez.

CD full mix track 3, backing tack 10: *Downtime*∗

This is a laid back funk tune à la Jamiroquai that features close chord work which requires precise picking hand control. There is an eight bar solo marked and you are also asked to vary the part during repeats.

Composer: Hussein Boon.

CD full mix track 4, backing track 11: *Queen for a Day*

Stadium rock in all its glory. The guitar part is quite straight forward with several pentatonic based licks and chord passages for you to get your teeth into. Give the harmonics plenty of whammy, and add as much feedback as you think is necessary.

Composer: Deirdre Cartwright. Deirdre fronted the TV *Rockschool* series in the 1980's and now plays and teaches guitar extensively across Europe.

CD full mix track 5, backing track 12: *In the Bag*

James Brown's influence can be felt throughout the history of popular music from Little Richard and Prince to modern funk players and even rap artists. This piece uses a lot trademark funk guitar figures, either dotted eighth/eighth note pairs or eighth/16th note combinations, along with trademark ninth chords in a variety of shapes.

Composer: Steve Wrigley: Steve is an exceptionally gifted guitarist and composer who has written a number of theatre and TV scores as well as playing for artists such as P J Proby, Bernard Purdie and Sarah Jane Morris.

CD full mix track 6, backing track 13: *Rock Steady*

A Rock & Roll tune in the style of Chuck Berry. The part is straightforward but don't allow the tempo to flag. An eight bar solo is marked at [A].

Composers: Dave Barnard. Dave began his career as a punk rocker before developing a taste for Latin music. He is now guitar player and MD for King Salsa and plays a lot throughout Europe.

CD Musicians:

> **Guitars:** Deirdre Cartwright and Hussein Boon on (*) **Bass:** Geoff Gascoyne
> **Drums:** Mike Bradley **Keyboards and programming:** Adrian York

Grade Exam Marking Scheme

The table below shows the marking scheme for the *Guitar* Grade 5 exam.

ELEMENT	PASS	MERIT	DISTINCTION
Piece 1 Piece 2 Piece 3	13 out of 20 13 out of 20 13 out of 20	15 out of 20 15 out of 20 15 out of 20	17+ out of 20 17+ out of 20 17+ out of 20
Technical Exercises	11 out of 15	12 out of 15	13+ out of 15
Either: Sight Reading *Or:* Improvisation & Interpretation	6 out of 10	7 out of 10	8+ out of 10
Ear Tests	6 out of 10	7 out of 10	8+ out of 10
General Musicianship Questions	3 out of 5	4 out of 5	5 out of 5
Total Marks	**Pass: 65% +**	**Pass: 75% +**	**Pass: 85% +**

Performer Zone Performance Certificate/Band Exam Marking Scheme

The table below shows the marking scheme for both the *Performer Zone* Performance Certificate and the *Performer Zone* Band Exam. You will see that the Pass mark for both is now **70%**. The Merit mark is **80%** and the mark for a Distinction performance is **90%**.

ELEMENT	PASS	MERIT	DISTINCTION
Piece 1	14 out of 20	16 out of 20	18+ out of 20
Piece 2	14 out of 20	16 out of 20	18+ out of 20
Piece 3	14 out of 20	16 out of 20	18+ out of 20
Piece 4	14 out of 20	16 out of 20	18+ out of 20
Piece 5	14 out of 20	16 out of 20	18+ out of 20
Total Marks	Pass: 70% +	Merit: 80% +	Distinction: 90% +

Free Choice Song Criteria

You can bring in your own performance pieces to play in any of the exams featured. In the Grade Exams you can bring in **one** piece.

In either the *Performer Zone* Performance Certificate or the *Performer Zone* Band Exam you may bring in up to **two** pieces. You should read the following criteria carefully.

- Players may bring in either their own compositions or songs already in the public domain, including hits from the charts.
- Songs may be performed either solo or to a CD or tape backing track.
- Players should bring in two copies of the piece to be performed, notated either in standard notation, chord charts or TAB. Players must use an original copy of the tune to be performed, and must provide a second copy for the examiner, which may be a photocopy. For copyright reasons, photocopies handed to the examiner will be retained and destroyed by Rock School in due course.
- Players may perform either complete songs or extracts: such as a solo part.
- Players should aim to keep their free choice songs below 2 minutes in length.
- *Player Zone* Band Exam parts should feature independent lines for all instruments.
- Players should aim to make each free choice song of a technical standard similar to those published in the Rockschool *Guitar* Grade 5 book. However, examiners will be awarding credit for how well you perform the song. In general players should aim to play songs that mix the following physical and expressive techniques and rhythm skills:

Physical Techniques: accurate left and right hand co-ordination; picking hand damping; alternate picking, use of double stops on adjacent strings, damping for percussive sounds, smooth string crossing when playing sixthes, sevenths and octaves.

Expressive Techniques: legato and staccato, a wide dynamic range (very soft to very loud), slides, fretting hand legato, hammer-ons and pull-offs, accented notes, comfortable slap style guitar both with and without dead notes.

Rhythm Skills: songs should contain a mixture of whole, half, quarter, eighth and 16th notes, dotted quarter notes and their associated rests. Songs should contain simple uses of syncopation and be in 4/4 time signatures with the occasional bar of different time signatures as required.

You, or your teacher, may wish to adapt an existing piece of music to suit the criteria above. You should ensure that any changes to the music are clearly marked on the sheet submitted to the examiner.

Entering Rockschool Exams

Entering a Rockschool exam is easy, whether for the Grade, the *Performer Zone* Performance certificate or the *Performer Zone* Band Exam. Please read through these instructions carefully before filling in the exam entry form. Information on current exam fees can be obtained from Rock School by ringing **020 8332 6303**

- You should enter for the exam of your choice when you feel ready.

- You can enter for any one of three examination periods. These are shown below with their closing dates.

PERIOD	DURATION	CLOSING DATE
Period A	1st February to 15th March	1st December
Period B	15th May to 31st July	1st April
Period C	1st November to 15th December	1st October

These dates will apply from 1st January 1999 until further notice

- Please fill in the form giving your name, address and phone number. Please tick the type and level of exam, along with the period and year. Finally, fill in the fee box with the appropriate amount. You should send this form with a cheque or postal order to: **Rockschool, Broomfield House, 10 Broomfield Road, Richmond, Surrey TW9 3HS.**

- When you enter an exam you will receive from Rockschool an acknowledgement letter containing your exam entry number along with a copy of our exam regulations.

- Rockschool will allocate your entry to a centre and you will receive notification of the exam, showing a date, location and time as well as advice of what to bring to the centre.

- You should inform Rockschool of any cancellations or alterations to the schedule as soon as you can as it is usually not possible to transfer entries from one centre, or one period, to another without the payment of an additional fee.

- Please bring your music book and CD to the exam. You may not use photocopied music, nor the music used by someone else in another exam. The examiner will stamp each book after each session. You may be barred from taking an exam if you use someone else's music.

- You should aim to arrive for your *Guitar* Grade 5 exam fifteen minutes before the time stated on the schedule.

- The exam centre will have a waiting area and warm-up facilities which you may use prior to being called into the main exam room.

- Each Rockschool grade exam and *Performer Zone* Performance Certificate is scheduled to last for 25 minutes. The *Performer Zone* Band Exam will last 30 minutes. You can use a small proportion of this time to tune up and get ready.

- About 2 to 3 weeks after the exam you will receive a typed copy of the examiner's mark sheet. Every successful performer will receive a Rockschool certificate of achievement.